Northern Ireland Poets

Edited By Jess Giaffreda

First published in Great Britain in 2018 by:

Young Writers
Remus House
Coltsfoot Drive
Peterborough
PE2 9BF
Telephone: 01733 890066
Website: www.youngwriters.co.uk

FOREWORD

Young Writers was established in 1991, dedicated to encouraging reading and creative writing in young people. Our nationwide writing initiatives are designed to inspire ideas and give pupils the incentive to write, and in turn develop literacy skills and confidence, whilst participating in a fun, imaginative activity.

Few things are more encouraging for the aspiring writer than seeing their own work in print, so we are proud that our anthologies are able to give young authors this unique sense of confidence and pride in their abilities.

For our latest competition, Rhymecraft, primary school pupils were asked to enter a land of poetry where they used poetic techniques such as rhyme, simile and alliteration to bring their ideas to life. The result is an entertaining and imaginative anthology which will make a charming keepsake for years to come.

Each poem showcases the creativity and talent of these budding new writers as they learn the skills of writing, and we hope you are as entertained by them as we are.

CONTENTS

Benjamin McKinley (11) 59
Aaron Shaw (9) 60

Dromore Road Primary School, Warrenpoint

Karim Zerai (9) 61
Lucas Williams (10) 62
Emilija Daksevic (9) 63
Edgaras Teriajevas (9) 64
Ashley Bedzeti (8) 65
Hannah Lawson (8) 66
Leah Cumming (10) 67
Brody Cumming (8) 68
Niks Teteris (10) 69
Rainers Miksons (9) 70

Drumgor Primary School, Brownlow

Kenzie Fitzsimmons (10) 71
Matilda Sherry (11) 72
Adam Chmielowicz (10) 73
Bethany Wilson (10) 74
Natalia Panczyk (11) 75
Gabriele Urbietyte (11) 76
Josh Harvey (11) 77
Tanya Mirska (11) 78
Dalma Szabo (11) 79
Jamie Whiteside (11) 80
Alan Stefanski (11) 81

Fourtowns Primary School, Ahoghill

Johanna Moody (9) 82
Carter Brown 84
Rebecca Faulkner (9) 86
Ben Clark (9) 88
Susanna Quigley (9) 89
Rachel Campbell (9) 90
Mya Neill (9) 91
Chloe Dowds (9) 92
Naomi McDowell (8) 93

Zac Conley (9) 94
Rachel Dickey (8) 95
Stephanie McKee (9) 96
Hannah McFarland (8) 97
Noah Parker (8) 98
Lydia Calderwood (9) 99
Scott Samuel Drummond (8) 100

Gaelscoil An TSeanchaí, Magherafelt

Diarmuid Ó Donnghaile (9) 101
Enya Patel (8) 102
Alan Wilinski (8) 103
Cormac O'Kane (8) 104
Zofia Gralewska-Begley (9) 105
Aoife O'Kane (8) 106
Evan Ross (9) 107

Gortin Primary School, Gortin

Ellie Louise Magee (10) 108
Stephen Mcilwaine (9) 109
Emma Orr (9) 110
Betha Rickford (8) 111
Alex Burton (10) 112
Andrea Joanne McConnell (9) 113
Sam Hempton (9) 114
Leah Campbell (9) 115

Greystone Primary School, Antrim

Abigail McMinn (8) 116
Lexi Curtis (8) 117
Daisy Moore (8) 118
Madison Michelle Keenan (8) 119
Catherine Wilde (8) 120
Max McClean (7) 121
Jasmine Stewart (8) 122
John Graham (8) 123
Harry Fisher (8) 124

Kingsmills Primary School, Whitecross

Dylan Robert Fegan (10)	125
Rachel King (11)	126
Lydia Burke (9)	127
Sophie Hamilton (10)	128
Poppy Alexandra McCormick (11)	129
Kacey Hamilton (9)	130
Reuben Revels (11)	131
William Flanagan (10)	132
Jessica Courtney (10)	133

Old Warren Primary School, Lisburn

Jessica Portis (9)	134
Jake Lyness (9)	135
Jayden Mcbride (8)	136
Tyler Cree (9)	137
Charlie Freddie Mitchell Paisley (9)	138
Faith Boal (8)	139
Sophia Apsley (9)	140
Jayden Atcheson (9)	141
Rhys Cummins (8)	142

Rathcoole Primary School, Newtownabbey

Savannah Morrison (10)	143
Kelechi Chima (9)	144
Casie Anne Boyd (10)	145
Hayley Taylor (11)	146
Ella Conroy (10)	147
Alicia Gray (11)	148
Abbie Louise Hamilton (10)	149

St Brigid's Primary School, Sixmilecross

Michéal Hugh Mullin (9)	150
Darren Owens (9)	151

St Mary's Primary School, Dungannon

Matthew McCallan (10)	152
Daniel McKearney (10)	153

THE POEMS

Candy Kingdom

I have appeared on an island made completely of
sugar,
I wonder what lives here?
I walk around the mountain and find a small cave,
I look into it and see six little chocolate dinosaurs,
Sweet as sugar, but fierce on the inside
I climb the mountain aboard the mighty
chocosaurus rex
I jump in a cloud only to find it's candyfloss,
I fall through the mountain down, down, down into
the treacle below,
I am stuck in the treacle
I sink to the bottom
I can no longer breathe, then
I hear a faint beeping noise
I wake with a start
I realise I am late for school and that it was all a
dream,
then I wonder, why was there a castle on a
deserted island?

Toby McClean (10)
Aughnacloy Primary School, Aughnacloy

Magic Forest Of Dreams

Once upon a time, in a big town,
an old, fat man was a king with a big, fat frown
Then the fairy dust went over,
the old man knew he wasn't getting any older

The fairies put a spell on him,
he was sent to a forest, dark and dim.
He felt the touch of winter at the end of his hands,
the whine of the wind put him in a trance

Wolves howled and growled at night,
but he could not find a light
Then, the great wolf came to make him beg on his
knees in shame,
wolves kept coming, again and again

Then he saw the light of dawn,
then he knew his time was nearly gone
He walked down the lane
and was in bad pain

The rain shook and shattered and the sky was in
tears,
the thunder shocked and shot the man quite some
light years

He sat on a curled star and saw his wife on another,
he tried to get over but it was a lot of bother

The stars faded away,
because it was day
He said he was done,
okay you've won.

Zara Law (11)
Aughnacloy Primary School, Aughnacloy

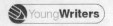
Horse Riding

H appy when riding my favourite chocolate-brown horse
O ver the jump I go, smiling all the way
R iding every day and also in my dreams
S hould I chance the higher jump?
E veryone claps when I clear the course and come first

R acing through the soft, green fields
I n the fields, I travel for miles, loving the wind in my hair
D own in the fields and over the hills, loving every second
I 'm jumping over the hedge now
N obody can stop me here, I am free!
G oing back home, will I come back tomorrow?

Emily Stinson (10)
Aughnacloy Primary School, Aughnacloy

The Nightmare Forest

I don't know the time,
but I keep hearing a chime
Then soon after, a high-pitched whine

I decide to follow the noise,
I hope it's just some silly boys
Someone has died here, maybe Alois

I begin to rustle through trees,
seeing bloodsucking bumblebees,
hiding beneath the leaves

Then out comes the bee queen,
looking very mean,
as she gathers her team

As I start to run,
my legs become numb,
it really isn't that fun

She circles my head,
filling me with dread,
then I fall over, dead!

Hannah Margret Atkinson (10)
Aughnacloy Primary School, Aughnacloy

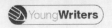

Hogwarts Castle

I arrive on platform 9¾ with much delight,
to get on board the green Hogwarts Express,
I wonder this year, will I get a fright,
or end up being a total mess?

When we arrive at Hogwarts castle,
I walk through the big, brown oak door
Hopefully this year won't be a hassle,
as I don't need detentions anymore!

As we walk into the great hall,
chatting away about our summer holidays
I hope my grades do not fall,
Hogwarts castle, I will remember always!

Victoria Rachel Sharkey (10)
Aughnacloy Primary School, Aughnacloy

The Underwater Nightmare Of Doom

Slippery serpents, swimming to hide,
I saw a dolphin let a turtle ride.
The water was getting colder,
by the minute, I was getting older

All the waves were crashing,
I saw a hurt fish splashing
I picked him up and swam,
Soon I would be raw ham

We got into a cave, with slimy seaweed,
I had to get out of this tangle, it was all I could need
Suddenly, I heard a bang, someone had slammed,
a door, it woke me, oh I'm still crammed!

Rebecca Graham (10)
Aughnacloy Primary School, Aughnacloy

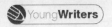

The Mystical Land Of Unicorns

The candy cane trees sway,
when the mystical unicorn flutters by
leaving a spray of glittery, magical, rainbow dust.
The gingerbread family,
are in the gingerbread house,
all eating a gingerbread mouse
The tiny, plump unicorns,
play happily in the candy cane forest,
while the mummy unicorn drinks
from the choco fall
Night falls, everyone is asleep,
not a thing to be heard,
at the Mystical Land of Unicorns

Jayne Bloomer (11)
Aughnacloy Primary School, Aughnacloy

Candy County

I see the flowing chocolate river,
running through the town
I smell sweet, sugary peppermint trees,
in the shape of candy canes
I feel the candyfloss grass,
is it as though I am walking on clouds
I taste the chewy caramel fudge,
that holds the houses up
I hear gummy bears singing and dancing,
because they've got some popping candy
This is the world I love,
I know you'd love it too.

Joanna Ashfield (10)
Aughnacloy Primary School, Aughnacloy

Animal Land

I look around and see animals,
cats, dogs, birds and camels
The sun is always shining,
and everyone is always smiling
I'm the only human in this land,
a cat plays the guitar in a kitten band
My friends are the cats, hamsters and mice,
sometimes the dogs get a lot of lice
I really like it here, I'm going back never,
this is Animal Land, I'll live here forever!

Lucy Falls (9)
Aughnacloy Primary School, Aughnacloy

The Perfect Utopia Land

Welcome to utopia for animals,
this place has no violence or cannibals
I have absolutely no idea how,
but there is not one single crossbred cow
This is the perfect utopia land,
the beaches are full of sand
Predators have no reason to kill,
because at twelve o'clock, their bellies fill
Birds soar in crowds through the air
and in his lair, is the hibernating bear.

Joshua David Ferguson (10)

Aughnacloy Primary School, Aughnacloy

The Real Life Of Under The Sea

H orrifying sounds underwater over the
O cean, people are screaming with fright
R eally, why does this have to happen to me?
R ed-eyed spiders stare at me
I am scared out of my wits, vampires with big
F angs, the werewolves are acting as though
I am their prey. The place is
C rowded with clowns cackling and going crazy.

Louise Marshall (10)
Aughnacloy Primary School, Aughnacloy

Candy Land

In Candy Lang there is no sand,
In Candy Land it is sweet and neat, it's a really
lovely treat
In Candy Land there's a marshmallow man
a lady that always needs a hand
There is a love tree, candy canes and frozen river
rain
The Curly Wurly bridge has got a nice taste
Mummy and I have just been chased
Enjoy and eat,
please don't lose your teeth!

Danielle Pike (10)
Aughnacloy Primary School, Aughnacloy

Every Day

In my little city, I make some videos,
Canon is the brand that I always use
Time to edit is at the end of the day,
before I choose to hit the hay
People think I'm weird because I do it every day,
in my studio where I always edit
Unfortunately, I have to do it every day,
at the end of the day in my room,
I have to hit the hay.

Matthew Alexander (11)
Aughnacloy Primary School, Aughnacloy

A Well-Known Pirate

Once I met a pirate,
he was really such a tyrant
His name was Davy Jones,
nothing to him but bones
When he calls you into the mist,
you simply cannot resist
He's cruel and vicious just like the sea,
he has no heart that's plain to see
So if your paths ever cross,
make sure you show him who is boss!

Ethan Quinn (11)
Aughnacloy Primary School, Aughnacloy

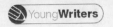

The Delicious Candy Land

Here in Candy Land,
everything is sweet
with houses made out of lollipops
and sugary drinks,
There are no bricks
Chocolate cakes make everything stick,
with grass made out of sprinkles
Clouds made out of candyfloss
I can't forget the Jammie Dodger sun,
all is good here in Candy Land.

Maddison Burgess (11)
Aughnacloy Primary School, Aughnacloy

Up To Snow Good

There was a little snowman,
who was called little Dan
He had a carrot nose,
and always did a pose
Little rabbit was his friend,
and each day he liked to pretend,
to take little Dan's nose,
and stuff it down the garden hose
Have fun today,
I'll be gone by May.

Alexandra Trotter (10)
Aughnacloy Primary School, Aughnacloy

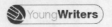

The Magical Land

Here is the magical land of fairies and unicorns,
there is a fairy called Pippa,
and a magical unicorn called Twinkle
Their houses are made from delicious candy,
with a sweet treat garden.
Clouds made from all the fluffy things in the world,
every little thing is in my big world.

Victoria Watters (11)

Aughnacloy Primary School, Aughnacloy

Candy Cane Lane

In Candy Cane Lane,
there are tiny cranes
I see a caramel wall,
which is really tall
There are trees,
that blow in the breeze
Which look like candyfloss
when the sun shines, they look like gloss
Tonight in Candy Cane Lane,
I'll go home in a candy plane.

Alana Joy Jamieson-Ewing (10)
Aughnacloy Primary School, Aughnacloy

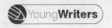

Dino Forest

In Dino Forest,
I eat porridge
It all smells good,
except for the wood
It doesn't bother me,
it's just a plain, old tree
In Dino Forest you can be free,
why don't you come and live with me.

Morgan Burgess (11)
Aughnacloy Primary School, Aughnacloy

Dance Land

Singing all throughout the land,
is the band that will follow your command
As they run across the land,
their magical band will expand
They have lots of fans,
who chase them across the sand.

Jack Coote Nixon (10)
Aughnacloy Primary School, Aughnacloy

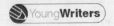

Farming

F arming is hard work
A nimals to be fed
R emember to keep safe
M anure to be spread
I n the field
N oise sometimes
G rass to grow.

Ethan Todd (12)
Aughnacloy Primary School, Aughnacloy

Emotions

Joy is... cheerful children, swimming energetically in the pool

Anger is... stupid cyclists, riding slowly in the middle of the road

Love is... adorable puppies, barking happily in the dog park

Unhappiness is... nasty bullies, kicking hurtfully at small children

Comfort is... helpful me, supporting P1s nicely when they fall

Shock is... rude children, shouting cheekily at their parents

Surprise is... exciting presents, waiting patiently for my birthday

Depression is... new phone, smashing violently on the ground

Gladness is... long holidays, coming quickly for me to enjoy

Alarm is... sneaky burglars, stealing quickly from my house.

Chloe Richmond
Ballytober Primary School, Bushmills

Emotions

Happiness is... enthusiastic cats, playing happily with me

Fear is... dead people, walking slowly through the cemetery

Joy is... a silly brother, dancing madly on the bed

Sadness is... little children, searching eagerly for presents

Trust is... happy passengers, relaxing contently on the aeroplane

Annoyance is... a daft mother, moving sneakily to hide all my Lego

Excitement is... massive roller coasters, shaking roughly on the track

Depression is... first day, driving slowly back to school

Comfort is... a tabby kitten, purring loudly in front of the fire

Anger is... an annoying brother, shouting crossly in my ear.

Joshua Dorrans
Ballytober Primary School, Bushmills

Emotions

Joy is... cuddly kittens, lying happily on top of me
Fear is... haunting ghosts, killing quickly in the
haunted mansion
Happiness is... inquisitive dogs, fetching amazingly
in the park
Shock is... scary ogres, running quickly after me
Satisfaction is... hygienic people cleaning properly
in the kitchen
Alarm is... energetic me, jumping awkwardly over
high fences
Comfort is... loving family, hugging me tightly in
the living room
Anger is... hateful gangs, shooting rapidly at
people in New York
Love is... kissing dolphins, swimming smoothly
through the sea
Grief is... little wasps, stinging nastily in the zoo.

Matthew Fox
Ballytober Primary School, Bushmills

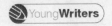

Emotions

Joy is... rough rugby players, running quickly on the pitch
Sadness is... an annoying brother, hitting firmly on my elbow
Love is... passionate hugs, landing wholeheartedly around each other
Anger is... a useless team losing sloppily in the match
Trust is... loyal friends, whispering truthfully to each other
Fear is... high rides, moving endlessly on the roller coaster
Delight is... delicious food, smelling beautifully in the kitchen
Shock is... cold water, splashing viciously on your face
Comfort is... fluffy blankets, wrapping tightly around me
Grief is... bad news coming unexpectedly to your family.

Alfie McFaull
Ballytober Primary School, Bushmills

Emotions

Joy is... energetic dogs, playing crazily at the park
Fear is... a cross mummy, shouting loudly at my
brothers
Trust is... nice friends, talking confidentially to me
all the time
Sadness is... young grannies, dying peacefully in
their house
Pleasure is... cheerful neighbours, playing fairly at
football
Anger is... annoying brothers, hitting angrily for no
reason
Delight is... a friendly uncle, laughing at my jokes
Shock is... dishonest people, stealing quickly to get
money
Happiness is... crazy pets, whirling madly, getting
tummy rubs
Stress is... annoying children, hitting nastily at a
party.

Dylan Pollock
Ballytober Primary School, Bushmills

Emotions

Joy is... fluffy sheep, bleating loudly in the back garden
Fear is... sick relatives, lying quietly in the hospital
Love is... a nice dad, hugging nicely every day
Envy is... funny children, acting daftly outside the house
Surprise is... a furry puppy, biting constantly on my fingers
Disgust is... disgusting vomit, lying nastily on the floor
Gladness is... a fantastic uncle, shopping quickly for my presents
Shock is... a rough brother, attacking noisily with Nerf guns
Willingness is... helpful me, tidying constantly in the classroom
Anger is... a nasty ferret, attacking nastily at my dad.

Tyra Gray
Ballytober Primary School, Bushmills

Emotions

Joy is... enthusiastic children playing happily in the park

Fear is... bad boys killing ferociously in our house

Trust is... good friends helping consistently with my work

Anger is... skilful teams losing badly in a match

Contentment is... delicious dinner, sitting on the table

Shock is... fluffy cats getting terribly injured on the road

Happiness is... crunchy crisps munching joyfully in a big mouth

Annoyance is... naughty children kicking harshly at footballs

Love is... loving couples, hugging tightly on their wedding day

Stress is... terrifying exams, waiting patiently to test you.

Charlie McCollum

Ballytober Primary School, Bushmills

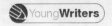

Emotions

Joy is... a bouncy football, rolling quickly towards the goal

Fear is... sad deaths happening slowly to my family

Trust is... a caring mum, hugging me tightly when I am sad

Anger is... a difficult homework, taking ages when I am tired

Comfort is... a red sofa, sitting nicely in my living room

Sadness is... an upset dad, crying loudly because Spurs got beaten

Love is... a happy family, waiting patiently for Christmas

Grief is... dead pets, buried secretly in my garden

Delight is... happy children, laughing noisily on their holiday

Disgust is... sad men, shooting nastily in our country.

Callum McKay
Ballytober Primary School, Bushmills

Emotions

Joy is... barking dogs, running happily around the park

Anger is... shouting Dad, stomping cheekily out the door

Happiness is... delicious chocolate, melting quickly in my mouth

Shock is... quick Ellen, crawling sleepily downstairs in the morning

Love is... adorable Jess, sleeping daftly in her bed

Sadness is... an angry mum, running to my room

Liveliness is... energetic music, playing loudly in the house

Fear is... fast cars, racing madly on the road.

Trust is... dependable God, waiting patiently in Heaven

Anxiety is... noisy Mrs A, running daftly into the car door.

Charlie Brown

Ballytober Primary School, Bushmills

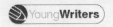

Emotions

Joy is... creepy jack-o'-lanterns, shining brightly on Halloween
Annoyance is... loud brothers, shouting constantly near me
Love is... a little brother, playing happily with me
Sadness is... cute pets, dying needlessly in my house
Excitement is... a little sister, walking easily towards me
Anger is... crying babies, waking noisily in the night
Pleasure is... polite children, speaking nicely to me
Disgust is... rude people shouting naughty words
Delight is... cute babies, playing nicely with my baby sister
Anxiety is... difficult poems performing quietly on stage.

Jamie McConaghy (11)
Ballytober Primary School, Bushmills

Emotions

Joy is... an amazing farmer, working happily on the
farm
Fear is... terrifying spiders, crawling slowly up my
arm
Delight is... fantastic models, sitting nicely at the
show
Anger is... annoying brother, punching harshly at
me
Trust is... a big daddy, shouting at David
Stress is... bad pains, hurting nastily on my back
Cheerfulness is... a great tractor, driving noisily
down the road
Shock is... a sore mummy, struggling patiently in
the hospital
Comfort is... cosy pyjamas, warming quickly on the
radiator
Anxiety is... difficult work, waiting quietly for me to
do.

Zach Termonia
Ballytober Primary School, Bushmills

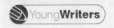

The Mystery Of The Missing Candy Cane

Welcome to Candy Land, where everything is made of sweets,
colourful and creative, everyone earns a treat
One day, a candy cane went missing, the unicorn was sad
He'd built his house and his cane, now he felt really bad
He looked in Snow Land, but nothing did he find
In Chocolate Land, he searched and searched, but nothing did he find
The colourful little unicorn trotted back to Rainbow Land,
he looked up high into the sky, where the rainbow began to shine,
and there at the end of the rainbow, his candy cane hung bright.

Sophie Francey (10)
Brookfield Special School, Moira

Nightmares Town

N uts will fall off the trees

I nside your bed will be eyeballs

G iant zombies will crush you

H ouses will have witches in

T urtles are skeletons

M ini insects are in your attics

A ngry clowns

R obots are dangerous in your living room

E normous caves are dark

S cary basements.

Kyle Clarke (9)

Brookfield Special School, Moira

My Minecraft World

My friends like my Minecraft world
I build lots of things in my Minecraft world
My city is really cool, I love my Minecraft world
I am so lucky to have my Minecraft world
There are tons of roads in my Minecraft world.
I sometimes build petrol stations and car washes.
I build statues in my Minecraft world.
Suddenly it's time for tea.

Sam Toner (11)
Brookfield Special School, Moira

Blue Planet Land

I see lots of rainbowfish in the sea
I hear clicking from the spinner dolphins
I dive into the open ocean to see colourful fish and
lanternfish
I smell different kinds of salty oceans
I feel wet after diving into the ocean
I see the blue shark in the open ocean
I catch a yellowfin tuna in the green seas
The Blue Planet amazes me.

Callum Purdy (11)
Brookfield Special School, Moira

The Skeleton Building

S keleton building Minecraft
K eeping blocks
E veryone building blocks
L oving Minecraft
E specially walls and houses
T ricky if you build it
O r cool, if it's something different
N ever ever go into Lava Land!

Shea Anthony Caddell (9)
Brookfield Special School, Moira

Candyland

C andy everywhere
A nd not a blade of grass
N ever not tasty
D reams are magical
Y eah, all day!
L ands are beautiful
A nd very tasty
N ear the chocolate river
D ive in and have some fun.

Jenna Boden (9)

Brookfield Special School, Moira

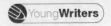

Minecraft

M inecraft is a game
I n it are blocks
N ames and animals
E ven though it's a game
C raft world
R aining drops
A nd now it's raining
F orever and ever
T ill the rain stops.

Ryan Noel Reynolds (10)
Brookfield Special School, Moira

Dreamy Land

D ads love dreaming because dreams come true

R ead dreamy land books, so stories come to life

E at dream foods from stories and tales

A t Dreamy Land, you can make dreams come
true

M ake everything come true.

Andrew James Houston (9)

Brookfield Special School, Moira

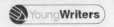

Funky Land, Evil Land

I hear happy children singing and volcanoes
erupting
I see dancing people and lazy people
I smell creamy candy canes and hot lava
I taste colourful Skittles and sour sweets
I touch candy trees and jaggy plants.
This is Mixture Land!

Jake Kane (10)
Brookfield Special School, Moira

Family Fun Land

In Family Fun Land, I hear my brother and sister
laughing
I see my mummy and daddy getting a tan
I smell spaghetti Bolognese when I come I home
from school
I taste spaghetti in my mouth
I touch love and feel it all around me.

Carla McArdle (10)
Brookfield Special School, Moira

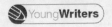

Gummy Bears Land

I hear happy gummies having fun
I see lots of chewy gummy bears
I smell all kinds of chewy sweets
I taste lots of soft gummy bears, lemon, lime and
strawberry
I touch all of the soft gummy bears and the other
sweets too.

Barry Rowan (11)
Brookfield Special School, Moira

Back To The Future

I hear gunshots from miles and miles away
I see white smoke fading away
I smell gunpowder and metal
I touch warm gun shells on the ground
I taste strong petrol dripping and dripping
The future is all around.

Rogan Rocks (11)

Brookfield Special School, Moira

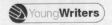

Proud City

I have built a city,
I am proud of it
My friends are so witty,
when we play it's a hit!

My friends love my city,
so they play there so much
I am happy,
Now, I'm off to lunch!

Cameron Mann
Brookfield Special School, Moira

Magic Land

M agic is real

A nd extraordinary

G rass is magical

I n Magic Land

C alm music

A ttracts children

L earning more about magic.

Blake Hill (9)

Brookfield Special School, Moira

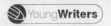

Castle Land

I hear knights fighting
I smell soup cooking
I hear swords swinging
I taste a big, tasty turkey
I touch cold bumpy walls
This is Castle Land!

Ben Glover (11)
Brookfield Special School, Moira

Halloween Land

It looks like scary pumpkins
It smells like sticky candy
It feels like sparklers
It tastes of toffee apples
It sounds like loud fireworks.

Kyle Benson (10)
Brookfield Special School, Moira

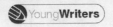
Pelé Dream

One dark night
I went to bed
I felt quite sick,
I'd bumped my head

Before I knew it
I was in a dream
I could hear
The crowd scream

I had scored
An overhead kick
I'd beaten the defender
I was so quick

I was Pelé
Playing for my team
In the World Cup
The best you've ever seen

The whistle blew
for half-time

I felt fit
In my prime

The manager said
"Play your best,
let's win the cup,
and beat the rest."

I scored two more
A volley and header,
I saw my name
In bright flashing letters

I heard the whistle
for the end of the game,
Brazil won three-nil
they were shouting my name

My alarm went off,
wait, where was I?
I was still in bed
where I tried to lie

I couldn't wait
to get to school,

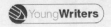

to tell my dream
they'd think it was cool

I told the teacher,
she said, "Don't be daft,
get on with your work,
today it's Minecraft."

I usually don't know,
how to make things rhyme
but thanks to my dream
I had ideas this time.

Cody-Lee McBurnie (11)
Clarawood Special School, Belfast

Chocolate World

C hocolate tastes great

H ouses are made from it

O ther lands aren't as good

C hocolate Land is made from food

O nly children are allowed

L aughing, joking all around

A never-ending river of treats

T ons of chocolate, jellies and sweets

E at until your bellies are full

L ots of activities which are cool

A nd lots of baking

N ight-time bring hot chocolate and milk

D ream of chocolate as soft as silk.

Jay Hart (10)

Clarawood Special School, Belfast

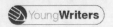

The Funny Gummy Poem

I've arrived in the land of candy,
where everything is fine and dandy

The rivers flow with honey,
and the trees are filled with money

Candy canes grow from the ground,
they don't even cost a pound,
that is why the place is sound

Nobody has ever had a frown,
Candy Land is the ultimate town.

Conor Coleman (10)
Clarawood Special School, Belfast

Noseworld

N ose like a hose

O h my gosh, Noseworld

S not comes out of the nose

E normous elephant trunk

W here noses

O f all shapes and sizes

R oam around

L ooking for faces

D o you want to go to Noseworld?

Samuel Ryan Rainey (9)

Clarawood Special School, Belfast

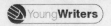

The Cannon

I hear winds blowing
I see tall trees and bumps everywhere
I smell fire burning
I taste the ash from the fire
I touch hot wood.

Karol Chmielewski (11)
Clarawood Special School, Belfast

Poor Itty Bitty

I n the bluebell forest,
T here were some big bad wolves
T here our cat, Itty Bitty, stood really scared
Y es things were not looking good for Itty Bitty.

B arney, the leader of the wolves, sent the other wolves to bite Itty Bitty
I tty Bitty was bitten by the wolves on the bum
T om, a friend of Itty Bitty, chased the wolves away
T his meant for Itty Bitty to say a big thank you to Tom
Y esterday, Itty Bitty got home from the vet because she was much better.

Yasmin Anna Fleming (7)
Cumran Primary School, Clough

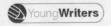

Fairy Land

A secret passage behind the tree,
come on, let's go, just you and me
You will see flowers, butterflies and rainbows too,
and a fairy sitting, looking at you
Bees getting nectar,
from flowers while frogs are leaping far
Bunnies hopping all around,
but they're so light you can't hear a sound,
so come on down to Fairy Land.

Christie Steele (8)
Cumran Primary School, Clough

I'm On The Moon

I'm on the moon
I can hear aliens building towers
I can see aliens talking to each other
I can taste the excellent food they make
I can smell the brilliant smell of the tasty food
I can touch the moon rocks all around the city
I'm on the moon.

Benjamin McKinley (11)
Cumran Primary School, Clough

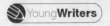

Rhyme Poem

In the village
Creeper came crawling
blew up village
tornado swirling,
lightning frightening,
thunder, *bang!*
destroyed the village.

Aaron Shaw (9)
Cumran Primary School, Clough

Mountain Moon

M ajestic, cool, magical and endless

O h, how much I love the priceless food

U ntil I hear the rocket ship's boom, I will stay on Mountain Moon

N ever ever will I be scared because I dared to come here

T here will never be a thing I will get bored of

A t the castle, there is a block of cheese

I n Mountain Moon, you can do the unimaginable

N ow you can do the unimaginable like jumping and doing a double flip

M ajestic as the Mourne Mountains, it might be good for you

O ver the stars, you'll find us waving at you

O n Mountain Moon, you'll find us there

N ear the stars, in mid-air.

Karim Zerai (9)

Dromore Road Primary School, Warrenpoint

Choco Land

C hoose your favourite food and candy
H ow wonderful it is here
O h, it's covered in every kind of delicious chocolate
C hocolate melting in my mouth like popping candy
O h wow, there's a giant chocolate fountain

L ovely sparkly water which is candy flavour too
A nd a giant chocolate castle on a Malteser hill
N ow why don't you come over?
D on't hesitate to visit the funniest place ever.

Lucas Williams (10)
Dromore Road Primary School, Warrenpoint

Smigglandia

S parkle shining seas like the sun
M y land is fun and yummy
I like to eat the candy canes
G lamorous mermaids swish their tales
G ood fun for everyone
L ovely chocolate smell everywhere
A beautiful mermaid is the queen!
N o one is mean in my land
D o you know there are diamonds?
I love my land
A mazing views of candy, diamonds and
mermaids in Smigglandia.

Emilija Daksevic (9)

Dromore Road Primary School, Warrenpoint

Money World

M aking money every second
O ver the views you see the sun shine
N ever have to work
E very morning it rains candy
Y ou can go to the castle and look at potions

W henever you sleep, you'll have money under
   your pillow
O ver cold, steep mountains
R iding in chocolate planes
L ighting fireworks
D ollars rain down with the sparks.

Edgaras Teriajevas (9)
Dromore Road Primary School, Warrenpoint

Christmastopia

You walk into this land and all you see,
are billions of sweets or even me!
I can smell all the chocolate,
candy rivers galore,
what will be next?
I can already taste the candy cane sticks
You can hear all the children licking the candy
canes
Then playing around,
You can touch the cold ice cream,
time to cool down
Take a rest,
Santa's coming to town.

Ashley Bedzeti (8)
Dromore Road Primary School, Warrenpoint

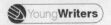

Unicorn Land!

U nicorns are my favourite animals

N ever-ending supply of cupcakes

I love cute unicorns

C olours are like ice cream

O h no, the unicorn has disappeared

R ainbow colourful snow

N o sadness in this place!

Hannah Lawson (8)

Dromore Road Primary School, Warrenpoint

Rainbow World

In Rainbow World,
Every girl's hair is curled,
We're all happy,
Not yappy,
The Skittles are yummy,
So tell your mummy,
Because everyone's a winner,
Sweets for dinner,
In the diner,
It's all finer.

Leah Cumming (10)
Dromore Road Primary School, Warrenpoint

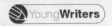

Sportsland

S weat running down your face
P edals turning and turning
O utstanding javelin competitions
R unning is an amazing sport too
T he swimming pool is nice and warm
S kating as fast as a light, I won!

Brody Cumming (8)
Dromore Road Primary School, Warrenpoint

The Dreamland

I hear kids laughing,
I see people bouncing on the trampoline,
I smell a burger sizzling,
I taste the fresh hot dogs,
I touch the cold swimming pool,
I love Dreamland!

Niks Teteris (10)
Dromore Road Primary School, Warrenpoint

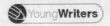

Sandyland

I can see the beautiful waves and sand,
I can taste the sweet water,
I can hear the dolphins,
I can feel the soft sand,
I can smell the barbecue.

Rainers Miksons (9)
Dromore Road Primary School, Warrenpoint

Birthday Land

B irthdays in my land are every day
I cing on the cakes are sweet like sherbet sticks
R ipping open presents full of surprises
T iptoeing into your parent's room
H opping onto their bed
D ashing down the stairs, waiting for some treats
A dventuring in the dark
Y our birthday is here!

L urking outside to find your birthday cake
A erials all around like in gymnastics class
N achos and other delicious snacks go
D own into my stomach!

Kenzie Fitzsimmons (10)

Drumgor Primary School, Brownlow

Candy Water Park

In Candy Water Park, everyone is welcome
Every girl and every boy
There are lots of things to taste,
and when you come you'll be filled with joy!
There is a seven-storey elevator
On it there's a personal waiter
The elevator has two sugary glass windows
They look like two eyes with a chocolate mouth,
and then you reach the top at last
There is a big, long water slide
and you'll make a massive *splash!*

Matilda Sherry (11)
Drumgor Primary School, Brownlow

Dreamland

D reamland is amazing, you can have anything you want

R eally if you don't believe me, you can go and see

E very building is made of lollipops

A nd every path of chocolate

M aybe even every animal is friendly

L and animals and water animals too

A nd even though they are extinct

N ever-ending fun

D reamland is where you go.

Adam Chmielowicz (10)

Drumgor Primary School, Brownlow

The Land Of Love

My land is never sad,
My land is always glad.
In my land you're always looked after,
In my land you're always cared for.

In my kingdom,
You're always welcome.
In my kingdom,
Arguments are seldom.

In my family,
We all love each other.
In my family,
We all work together.

Bethany Wilson (10)
Drumgor Primary School, Brownlow

74

My Magical Christmas

C hristmas is my favourite festival
H appy holidays
R eindeer are special
I love Santa and his elves
S anta is always here for me
T o be happy on the land, eat sweets
M y land is full of gifts
A lways happy Christmas is here
S o everybody plays fair.

Natalia Panczyk (11)
Drumgor Primary School, Brownlow

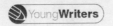
Music City

In Music City,
it is really bitty
Musicians play,
Every single day
Fairies like to sing,
to the great music king
Music pirates on their ship,
going on a musical trip
Records playing
People swaying,
"It's extraordinary!"
Please come visit us
Just take a music bus!

Gabriele Urbietyte (11)
Drumgor Primary School, Brownlow

In The Street

S omewhere in my city, engines are roaring loudly
T yres are screeching like banshees
R oads have skid marks everywhere
E veryone is cheering for the race
E verybody is crowding up the place
T oo many motorbikes in this case.

Josh Harvey (11)
Drumgor Primary School, Brownlow

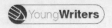

Rainbow Land

Everything is colourful, nothing is sad,
Everything is happy in Rainbow Land,
Nightmares are banned and dreams come true,
The buildings are candy as fluffy as clouds,
Everyone is happy and the music is loud in
Rainbow Land!

Tanya Mirska (11)
Drumgor Primary School, Brownlow

Busy Land

Everyone is really busy in the sunny mornings
In Busy Land there are a lot of people
As I'm sitting on this bench,
I hear people chattering happily
Dogs are growling and barking
And I am proud of our busy land!

Dalma Szabo (11)
Drumgor Primary School, Brownlow

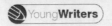

Cheeseland

C heddar, cheddar cheese
H as it been cooked? Can I have it please?
E ven full of this
E ven show your cheesy bliss
S till love cheese
E dam is a type of this.

Jamie Whiteside (11)
Drumgor Primary School, Brownlow

Space Is Here!

S hining stars all around
P lanets going up and down
A nd my land is close by
C astles and creatures
E volve nearby.

Alan Stefanski (11)

Drumgor Primary School, Brownlow

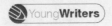

Magic Kingdom

In the Magic Kingdom, everything is fun,
people play every day in the sun,
All the animals talk,
and the sneaky witches stalk.

In the lovely, music wood,
they have singing food,
The dragons are fiery red,
and their babies must be fed.

The king and queen have magical powers,
and their garden is filled with magical flowers
At the candy street,
you will find a yummy treat.

At the top of the Unicorn Mountain,
there are lovely rainbow fountains
The phoenix is orange, yellow and red
and it raises the sun to get you out of bed.

At the Magic Royal Castle,
there is always lots of hassle

In the ocean are jewels and pearls,
and in the ocean the octopus swirls.

The dolphins would splash about,
and people only fish for trout
Now you really can be sure,
that the Magic Kingdom is filled with adventure.

Johanna Moody (9)
Fourtowns Primary School, Ahoghill

Campville

Welcome to Campville, a lovely land,
everyone loves it because it has its own band
Campville has lovely games to play,
with a lovely tent bay

Every raindrop looks like tents, can't you see?
All the shops shoot out blue bumblebees,
In the shops, there are excellent toys,
Just for your little girls and boys

There are even rides like ziplines and boats,
and a giant tent with its own moat
There are tent-shaped TVs there,
and tablets shaped as a sphere

We made wooden tents on top of our trees,
so you can really feel the breeze
Campville has a tent of chatter,
For all the people who matter

Can you find the hidden playground?
Shh! It's under the waterfall with a wonderful
merry-go-round

I love this land more than my mouse,
that I want to build it at my house.

Carter Brown

Fourtowns Primary School, Ahoghill

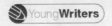

Forest Adventure

In the forest, woodland creatures play,
they sound like cats miaowing,
they have new adventures every day

The forest creatures jump and run,
in their play park,
they have lots of fun

In the forest, there are pine trees,
grumpy, old, grizzly bears,
and buzzy honeybees

The baby bears cuddle up to Mummy,
with their bellies full
of yummy honey

The busy bees inside their hive,
are making honey
to survive

I hear the crunching of the leaves,
as Leaf Man walks,
through the trees

The forest creatures look up high,
as the mighty forest whale
glides through the sky.

Rebecca Faulkner (9)

Fourtowns Primary School, Ahoghill

Dino Land

In Dino Land, I can see a Carasaurus,
driving all over town, being a crazy dino
There are dino people,
in their humble, coconut homes

In the land, I can hear all the dinosaurs,
They're quite crazy and I haven't slept for a whole
fortnight
In the land, I can smell dinochildren,
who haven't been bathed for weeks,
they're really smelly,
and I can't stand it

In the land, I can taste dinopops,
they're dino-delicious,
In the land, I can touch the scaly dino's back,
it makes me shake.
I feel sad because I never want to leave,
I wish I could stay one more dino-night.

Ben Clark (9)
Fourtowns Primary School, Ahoghill

Frozen Land

Frozen Land, Frozen Land
See the shimmering snowflakes fall
Onto the snowy trees so tall
snowy, frosty, cold and slippery
The musical birds sing tunes to me
way up high in the frosty tree.
Children skating, playing, laughing, having so much fun
in the snowy weather, instead of the summery sun
It's like a blizzard when the snow falls
outside I hear the birds' melodious calls
A child sits beside the flaming fire
she comes from the cold, she is tired
As the icicles melt outside,
her tired eyes open wide
For across the room, what can she see?
A neatly wrapped present, under the tree.

Susanna Quigley (9)
Fourtowns Primary School, Ahoghill

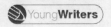

Fairytopia

In Fairytopia, the sky is blue,
and it has a big petting zoo
The fairies fly oh so high,
as they deliver their rainbow pie

The queen has a big house,
and she has a green pet mouse
The fairies sound lovely as they sing,
they can win a prize called the Magical Ring

All the shops sell lots of wings,
and all the wings have a lot of bling
The queen's house is white as snow,
but it gives off a slightly warm glow

The clouds are white, white as paper,
but I'll talk about that later
My trip to Fairytopia has been quite grand,
it is such a brilliant land.

Rachel Campbell (9)
Fourtowns Primary School, Ahoghill

Christmas Candy Land

C hristmas Candy Land here I come!
H ow I'll have so much fun
R eally busy all around
I t's even busy underground
S houting, "Santa, please, please come!"
T he children shout as they run
M um and I have a surprise
A s we open up our eyes
S anta said, "You'd better be good!

C ome and get some of Santa's food
A nd you'll see me ride on my sleigh
N ot just yet, on Christmas Day!"
D eer fly in the sky at night,
Y es, it's such an amazing sight!

Mya Neill (9)
Fourtowns Primary School, Ahoghill

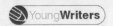

Hot Chocolate Land

H ot chocolate is boiling in the hot chocolate river

O utburst marshmallow explosion!

T he chocolate is melting from the steam

C ocoa is falling from the sky

H ow marshmallow is drizzling along the ground

O utrageous hot chocolate is very delicious

C an you smell the scent all around?

O f the sweetness of the chocolate trees?

L and of chocolatey dreams

A chocolate man is waving, "Hi!"

T he clouds are made out of marshmallows

E very time you visit Hot Chocolate Land, your dreams will come true.

Chloe Dowds (9)

Fourtowns Primary School, Ahoghill

Candy Land

In Candy Land, I can see,
Lots of sweets in front of me,
When I eat them they go in my tummy,
and they are very, very yummy

The Candy Land king sees me now,
but I really don't know how
What way should I run now, because I am confused,
the Candy Land king doesn't look amused

The fudge is so soft and it melts in your mouth,
I can also see a gingerbread house
Also, there are chocolate walls,
that are very, very tall

This is a delightful land,
and it was very grand
I want to stay for one more week,
but I'm so tired, I cannot speak.

Naomi McDowell (8)
Fourtowns Primary School, Ahoghill

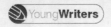

The Pirate Island

On Pirates Island, I can see,
ships sailing past me
I jump aboard a ship one day,
and say to the captain, "Let's go away!"

The cove is really cool,
I wonder if there is a pool
I go to the cove one day,
next time I go, I will stay

The red wreck is really weird,
I wonder if anybody on it has a beard
I jump on top of the very old wreck,
I hurt my knee and it aches

I go to see Captain Cutlass,
and his pet parrot called Douglas
Captain Cutlass lives on the red rocks,
he wears a pair of smelly socks.

Zac Conley (9)
Fourtowns Primary School, Ahoghill

Magical And Mystical

This is the magical and mystical world of fun,
Ask these witches and they'll conjure you up a bun,
As you can see there is a flying cat,
But wait, it's wearing a wizard's hat
The witches are flying high in the air, woah!
How high can they go?
There are lots of cauldrons everywhere,
But can you spot one bubbling brew there?
You now know about the amazing world of Magic
and Mystery
It surely will go down in history!

Rachel Dickey (8)
Fourtowns Primary School, Ahoghill

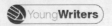

Little Snow Land

Little Snow Land, frozen pond,
the icicle ice is upon my wand
I see the beautiful sparrows rest,
in their lovely, cosy nest
And when I look up into the sky,
the ice will shimmer way up high
I feel the air as cold as snow,
I wish I could blow it right off my nose
An elegant butterfly swooped past my eye,
trying to steer her way into the sky
Next winter, I will see the same,
a beautiful land, so pure and tame.

Stephanie McKee (9)
Fourtowns Primary School, Ahoghill

Fairy Tales

F airies are pretty with their colourful clothes
A nything can happen any time
I f you make a wish
R apunzel cooks and paints magically
Y ou should see her beautiful hair!

T inker Bell flutters from place to place
A ll the time, making lovely friends
L ittle baby dragons
E veryone loves them
S moking little puffs of smoke out of their nostrils.

Hannah McFarland (8)

Fourtowns Primary School, Ahoghill

War World

W onderful houses are getting crushed
A load of bricks are falling
R iots of men coming with bombs

W ar never stops in War World
O utside there are bodies on the floor
R ockets are breaking the houses
L egs often get broken in War World
D efences are high and it's hard to break through.

Noah Parker (8)
Fourtowns Primary School, Ahoghill

Music Theatre

Come to my musical theatre,
I hope to see you later
Every day the orchestra plays,
and brightens all of our days

Pleasant sounding violins,
resting under people's chins
Making people fall asleep,
like a bird, when it tweets.

Lydia Calderwood (9)
Fourtowns Primary School, Ahoghill

Magic Castle

I see the dull, grey clouds in the sky above me
I hear the frightening thunder, crashing down on me
I taste the yummy pumpkin pie, brought by this old wizard
I smell the smoky air, coming from the cauldron
I feel my wand made of unicorn horns.

Scott Samuel Drummond (8)
Fourtowns Primary School, Ahoghill

Five Nights At Freddy's And Fantastic Saturn

(Haiku poetry)

Five Nights At Freddy's
Five Nights At Freddy's
I think it is brilliant
It is very fun.

Fantastic Saturn
It can be a peach
It is the second biggest
It is very cold.

Diarmuid Ó Donnghaile (9)

Gaelscoil An TSeanchaí, Magherafelt

Jupiter And Winter
(Haiku poetry)

Jupiter
It's the fifth planet
Jupiter is amazing
Has fifty-three moons.

Winter
Snow falls from the sky
The white snow falls on the ground
The white mornings come.

Enya Patel (8)
Gaelscoil An TSeanchaí, Magherafelt

Venus And Dragons

(Haiku poetry)

Venus
Venus turns brightly
Venus is made out of rock
Venus shines brightly.

Dragons
Dragons breathed fire
People were scared of dragons
Dragons used to live.

Alan Wilinski (8)
Gaelscoil An TSeanchaí, Magherafelt

Earth And Dogs

(Haiku poetry)

Earth
Earth is where I live
It is the big, blue planet
We have just one moon.

Dogs
Dogs are so crazy
Dogs are so small and fluffy
Dogs are very cute.

Cormac O'Kane (8)
Gaelscoil An TSeanchaí, Magherafelt

Saturn And Fairy Land

(Haiku poetry)

Saturn
Saturn is so cool
Saturn is in outer space
It's the sixth planet.

Fairy Land
Fairies do magic
As pretty as a princess
Abracadabra!

Zofia Gralewska-Begley (9)
Gaelscoil An TSeanchaí, Magherafelt

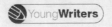

Earth And Dogs
(Haiku poetry)

Earth
Earth is where I live
It is the big, blue planet
We have just one moon.

Dogs
Dogs are very loud
Dogs are just adorable
Dogs are so friendly.

Aoife O'Kane (8)
Gaelscoil An TSeanchaí, Magherafelt

Mercury And The Dragon

(Haiku poetry)

Mercury
Mercury is hot
Found in the solar system
I love Mercury.

Dragon
The dragon is cool
While it plays the piano
It wears cool black shades.

Evan Ross (9)
Gaelscoil An TSeanchaí, Magherafelt

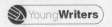

Nightmare Land

Night falls when the monsters come out
It is still and soundless in the night
Give a loud roar and children shout
All are standing with fear
The monsters standing just behind

Mummies coming out of tombs
All the land, standing weightless
Round the land, monsters smiling
Each and everyone looking fearful
Sound of gritting teeth together

Waiting for a tap on your shoulder
The sun creeps up behind the darkness
Lighting up Nightmare Land
The monsters slowly fade away
Nightmare Land waits for a new day.

Ellie Louise Magee (10)
Gortin Primary School, Gortin

Sports Land

Come to my Sports Land,
where you do high jumps on to the sand
People play with you all day long,
playing football, sing a winning song

Come to my Sports Land,
swimming in lanes as fast as you can
Jumping off boards and diving in,
looking underwater and seeing legs and arms

Come to my Sports Land,
people playing basketball and jumping
Scoring and getting a goal,
players so tall, they touch the sky.

Stephen Mcilwaine (9)
Gortin Primary School, Gortin

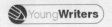

Magic Land

Magic Land is the most fun land of all,
you can have lots of fun,
playing games,
even with a magic wand

Magic school is so cool,
you can do sports, like jumping in sand,
but the most fun part is,
you do magic in this land

So come and live in magic land,
before the magic fades
You can do spells like making a great dinner
or even magic yourself to wherever you like.

Emma Orr (9)
Gortin Primary School, Gortin

Gymnastics Land

Come round here to Gymnastics Land,
flip and spin onto the sand.
Triple twists off the vault,
try and do it without a fault.

Splits, cartwheels, handstands too,
backflips, front flips, whoopie doo!
Beams, mats, bars galore,
have fun spinning and do some more.

Jump off beams,
flip off the bars,
follow your dreams,
and reach for the stars.

Betha Rickford (8)
Gortin Primary School, Gortin

Roblox World

Roblox is a land where you do battles and
make games
Games like jail break,
are some that you make
Or work at a pizza place,
customize your character and face
In the catalogue,
if you want, you can look like a dog
Make a good friend,
play until the end.

Alex Burton (10)
Gortin Primary School, Gortin

Friends Land

F riendly friends in Friends Land

R ound the land, friends join together

I hear happy kids playing

E verything is fun

N oisy games being played

D ancing around with each other

S o come and join us in Friends Land.

Andrea Joanne McConnell (9)

Gortin Primary School, Gortin

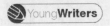

Theme Park Land

In Theme Park Land,
You can hear joyful kids on rides,
I see roller coasters, fast and twisty,
I can smell sweets from the candy stalls,
I taste the popcorn, sweet and salty,
I touch the smooth paint work of the rides
I love Theme Park Land.

Sam Hempton (9)
Gortin Primary School, Gortin

Football Land

Football friends
Having fun,
Come and join
everyone

We pick teams
start the match,
dribble and pass
to each other

If we win
we sing a song,
shake hands
and say, "Well done!"

Leah Campbell (9)
Gortin Primary School, Gortin

The Strange Woods

Please, please don't come here,
for soon you will be running in fear.
In the bush, there is a fairy,
but behind the tree is someone hairy!
It looks a bit like a bear,
oh, this is a horrid nightmare!
You'll scream and say, "I want to go home!"
But you will find you're all alone.
There is no place to rest your head,
for there is nothing that acts like a bed.
You will be shouting, "Why did I come in here?"
The reason is, you had no fear.

Abigail McMinn (8)
Greystone Primary School, Antrim

Underwater Magic

Come to my land to see the fish,
and hear the mermaid's tail swish
The jellyfish don't sting,
not even a little, not a thing
the octopus is orange and scary,
eight tentacles, but not a bit hairy
All the sharks won't cause you no harm,
they won't bite you, not even your arm
The whales are beautiful and big,
but don't stand too close, they could blow off
your wig
Come to my land, it's so much fun,
plenty to do for everyone.

Lexi Curtis (8)
Greystone Primary School, Antrim

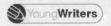
About Pirates

Pirates can be very sneaky
When they are trying to find some loot
Buried treasure, where can it be?
Use a map, just take a look
Follow the journey, it's easy to do
X marks the spot
Who will find it, you?

Daisy Moore (8)
Greystone Primary School, Antrim

Candy Land

Candy Land is made of sweets,
fizzy stuff, candyfloss; lots of treats.
Beautiful colours everywhere,
so much candy for us to share.
Come and visit this fabulous place,
enjoy the treats, stuff your face!

Madison Michelle Keenan (8)

Greystone Primary School, Antrim

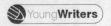

Unicorn Land

In Unicorn Land, everything is colourful,
you will see fairies baking and having fun
Collect their poo, it's made from Skittles,
Play sports, collect magic hair, fun for everyone.

Catherine Wilde (8)
Greystone Primary School, Antrim

Untitled

Chocolate Land is wonderful
It is really grand
Rich, brown chocolate
Running all around
Beautiful cakes, lots of buns
Delicious and sweet for everyone.

Max McClean (7)

Greystone Primary School, Antrim

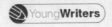

Candy

Sugary sweet, golden treats
Chocolate lakes and gummy snakes
Chocolate flakes go down a treat
My Candy Land is filled
With gummy sour sweets.

Jasmine Stewart (8)
Greystone Primary School, Antrim

Money Land

Money Land is really rich
The pigs are shiny and gold
The hotels are fancy and touch the sky
All that you see is gold.

John Graham (8)
Greystone Primary School, Antrim

Untitled

The dinosaurs are hungry
They want to eat me up
They're walking by the campfire
Ready to pounce, yum yum!

Harry Fisher (8)
Greystone Primary School, Antrim

Pizza Land!

P izza Land is very yummy, when the pizza is in your tummy

I like Hawaiian, mozzarella, margherita, pepperoni, thin and crispy, tomato sauce, nice and thick

Z ero healthy, gooey cheese, pineapple, sweetcorn, mushroom, onion, peppers, ham and chicken

Z igzagged lanes are sauce rivers of your choice, what a treat that's fun to eat

A t Pizza Land, there's only one shape, three edges that are pizza slices.

Dylan Robert Fegan (10)
Kingsmills Primary School, Whitecross

Underwater World

In my underwater world,
it's as beautiful as can be
Colonies of tiny animals,
have built coral reefs

Mermaids sit and sing their song,
their hair is blonde and tails are long
Dolphins dive down happily,
there's lots of creatures in the sea

In my underwater world,
all the fish gleam bright
In my underwater world,
they lighten up the night.

Rachel King (11)
Kingsmills Primary School, Whitecross

Animals

A nimals are cute

N ever give up looking after your animals

I love animals, my favourite animal is a lamb

M ilk the cows twice a day

A nimals can be very angry sometimes, especially bulls

L ambs are white, cute and fluffy

S ome animals are very, very special, I like guide dogs who guide blind people.

Lydia Burke (9)

Kingsmills Primary School, Whitecross

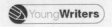

Pony City

In Pony City,
nothing was a pity.
It was all so pretty,
here in Pony City.

There was a pony called Jessie Jay,
she was cheeky, they would say.
She would rear,
and drink the odd beer.

Her best friend was Sparky
who was often very larky.
She was very funny,
and loves to chase my bunny.

Sophie Hamilton (10)
Kingsmills Primary School, Whitecross

Breakfast Town

In Breakfast Town,
there'll be no sign of a frown,
with toasted doors,
and chocolate floors

The walls are bacon,
milkshakes shaken,
the beans and rice,
are extra nice

So come on down,
to Breakfast Town,
I promise it's yum,
hope you have fun.

Poppy Alexandra McCormick (11)
Kingsmills Primary School, Whitecross

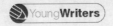

Footastic

F ootball, fab sport

O h! Over the bar

O h! I scored!

T ouch and go

B alls, no

A ww, unlucky

L ovely listening

L ovely goal

L ast minute

A nd...

N early...

D one!

Kacey Hamilton (9)
Kingsmills Primary School, Whitecross

The Acrostic Cupcake

C akes are delicious
U sually sweet
P arty treats
C herry topping
A ll delicious
K eep safe
E veryone eat

L ip licking
A ll enjoyed
N aughty but nice
D rizzle cake.

Reuben Revels (11)

Kingsmills Primary School, Whitecross

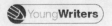

Rugby World

R ugby is what they play,
U sually to the end of the day,
G oing from one end of the pitch to the other,
B ringing their boots, not a bother,
Y esterday's zeros, tomorrow's heroes.

William Flanagan (10)
Kingsmills Primary School, Whitecross

My Unlucky Unicorn

I once rode a rainbow unicorn,
who stood on a very big thorn,
but when she got free,
she bent on one knee,
then let out a sneeze,
and galloped off over the sea.

Jessica Courtney (10)
Kingsmills Primary School, Whitecross

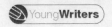

Friend Land

In Friend Land,
I see the friends hugging and playing nicely,
I hear the friends laughing loudly and having
fantastic fun,
I smell the scrumptious chocolate that the children
are eating,
I feel really excited in Friend Land.

In Friend Land,
I love that everybody is having fun and everybody
is happy,
I taste the chocolate that the friends are eating,
I hear the children play with their dog and snuggle
with their kittens,
This is what happens in Friend Land.

Jessica Portis (9)
Old Warren Primary School, Lisburn

Happy Land

M y land is made of fries
C aramel is my favourite drink
H appy Meals are falling from the sky
A pple pie is what I'm eating
P retty ice cream with sprinkles
P erfect, I'm happy
Y es, I got ice cream

L ollipops are so nice
A pple juice is so nice
N uts are the best in the burger
D rinks are the best.

Jake Lyness (9)
Old Warren Primary School, Lisburn

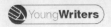

Candy City

In Candy City,
everything is sweet
It all tastes great,
not a speck of cool candy

There isn't one brick,
blue candy makes it sick,
there's a candy river,
the gummy snakes can slither

The trees are still green,
but they are filled with a cream,
come and visit this place,
where you can stuff your face with candy

Come and visit Candy City.

Jayden Mcbride (8)
Old Warren Primary School, Lisburn

Game Land

In Game Land, you can feel the pixely trees, waving around.

In Game Land, you can see FIFA players kicking a ball around the place.

In Game Land, you can touch glamorous guns and shoot pleasant players.

In Game Land, you can smell the taste of pizza, it's so good.

In Game Land, you can play Fortnite, Pac-Man, Minecraft, Roblox, Call of Duty and more.

Tyler Cree (9)
Old Warren Primary School, Lisburn

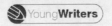

McDonald's Land

Every day is McDonald's in my world
I hear happy children eating crunchy chicken
nuggets
I see oily chips falling from the sky
I smell the oil of the chips cooking
I taste the chunky chicken
I touch the tasty Happy Meals
I love McDonald's.

Charlie Freddie Mitchell Paisley (9)

Old Warren Primary School, Lisburn

Sweetie Land

S crumptious pear drops, falling on me

W et, giant gummy bears sticking to my feet

E veryone filling their faces

E verything bursting into puddles of sweets

T he slippy sweets sticking all over me.

Faith Boal (8)

Old Warren Primary School, Lisburn

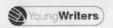

Crazy Chocolate Land

Candy is so handy, you could eat it every day
You don't need to pay,
you could smell the wonderful
chocolate from far away
I love to eat chocolate a lot,
it is so nice for dinner.

Sophia Apsley (9)
Old Warren Primary School, Lisburn

Game Kingdom

In Game Kingdom, I hear Pac-Man,
In Game Kingdom, I smell victory,
In Game Kingdom, I feel buttons,
In Game Kingdom, I taste pizza,
In Game Kingdom, I see everyone in a game.

Jayden Atcheson (9)
Old Warren Primary School, Lisburn

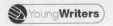

Magic Land

This is my land of wonder,
there is no thunder
There is good vs evil,
and magic seagulls
It's my magic place,
there is always a new face.

Rhys Cummins (8)

Old Warren Primary School, Lisburn

Tortoise Town

T ortoises are roaming in Tortoise Town
O ther animals are banned from this land!
R unning races, playing games and eating flowers
T hey even have a great rock band!
O ver the field, they get their magic powers
I n their shells is where they sleep
S ilver and gold in their pockets they keep
E very tortoise is special, they sound lovely when
they speak.

Savannah Morrison (10)

Rathcoole Primary School, Newtownabbey

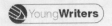

Creative City

In Creative City, you can build anything like houses,
food, cars, treats and lots more,
You can also be anything in Creative City,
You can use your imagination and build and do
anything you want,
In Creative City, everyone's houses are chocolate
cake because in Creative City, no one eats
chocolate cake,
In Creative City, there is a big mall, but you're only
allowed inside if you have a friend.

Kelechi Chima (9)
Rathcoole Primary School, Newtownabbey

Chocolate City

There was a little girl who walked into Chocolate City,
everything looked so pretty
Chocolate is sweet and so good to eat,
I like it whenever I need a good treat
In brownies and cookies and chocolate cake,
it adds extra sweetness to everything
You can bake with white chocolate, dark chocolate and milk chocolate galore,
I know I could eat a hundred pieces or more.

Casie Anne Boyd (10)
Rathcoole Primary School, Newtownabbey

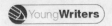

Glitter Land

Mermaids and fairies, unicorns fly free,
this magical wonderland is not make-believe
It's amazing and fun-filled, as you will see,
no nastiness or bullying you will find here
We can all live together, without any fear
So come with me to Glitter Land,
where life is not bitter
It's just filled with rainbows,
and lots of colourful glitter.

Hayley Taylor (11)
Rathcoole Primary School, Newtownabbey

Milkshake City

In Milkshake City, everything is so yummy, yum,
yum, yum.
There's a river made of strawberry milkshake,
a castle made of three extra large milkshake
glasses,
a princess milkshake unicorn and chocolate
buttons for stepping stones,
to get from the island to the castle.
This city is awesome. I am for sure coming back
here very soon.

Ella Conroy (10)

Rathcoole Primary School, Newtownabbey

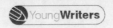
Into The Jungle

Into the jungle I go, counting my footsteps below
Monkeys swinging past, you see them in a flash
While sticks are breaking, the rivers are shaking
Crocodiles snapping, and birds being happy.

Alicia Gray (11)
Rathcoole Primary School, Newtownabbey

Friends City

As we get old,
friends come and go,
but my true friends stay,
that I'm glad to have
I have my friends,
that I know,
will be there forever.

Abbie Louise Hamilton (10)
Rathcoole Primary School, Newtownabbey

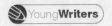

Christmas Memories

Daddy telling stories on Christmas Eve,
of Santa and what he has to achieve.
Mummy in the kitchen, preparing the Christmas dinner,
thinking she's a famous singer!

The rest of us are getting ready for Santa's arrival,
cookies, milk and if he's lucky, some trifle
Dark at night while Santa is in flight,
all the sleeping children, wishing they could see the magical sight.

Excited children jumping out,
waking their parents with a loud shout
Rallying down the stairs,
like wild hares.

Did Santa think we were bad or good,
did he eat all the food?

Michéal Hugh Mullin (9)
St Brigid's Primary School, Sixmilecross

My Wolf

Me and my grey, furry friend,
love each other to the end

We hunted down mobs together,
and tried to stop them from spawning forever

Then one terrible night,
there were too many mobs to fight

Using all of our might,
we tried to rid them from our sight

I slayed monster after monster,
but I was still outnumbered

I became so wary,
and I couldn't fight any longer

My wolf saved the day,
but bloody and lifeless he laid

For he sacrificed himself,
so I wouldn't lose any more health.

Darren Owens (9)
St Brigid's Primary School, Sixmilecross

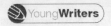

The Rainforest

The rainforest is an adventurous place
the monkeys swing, the tigers roar,
parrots fly, sloths climb,
snakes slither, frogs ribbit,
chameleons change colour,
ants build holes,
centipedes and millipedes,
exotic plants and trees,
snakes lurk in the grass,
but under the cave,
toucans are in the highest trees,
frogs leap out of leaves.

I think the rainforest is for me.

Matthew McCallan (10)
St Mary's Primary School, Dungannon

Dino Land

D eadly T-rex

I t is beautiful

N aughty brachiosaurus

O ld archaeopteryx

S ome as big as the Eiffel Tower

A nd some are as small as a newt

U proarious throughout the land

R aces happening all through the land

S o my land is really beautiful.

Daniel McKearney (10)

St Mary's Primary School, Dungannon

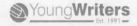

YOUNG WRITERS INFORMATION

We hope you have enjoyed reading this book – and that you will continue to in the coming years.

If you're a young writer who enjoys reading and creative writing, or the parent of an enthusiastic poet or story writer, do visit our website **www.youngwriters.co.uk**. Here you will find free competitions, workshops and games, as well as recommended reads, a poetry glossary and our blog.

If you would like to order further copies of this book, or any of our other titles, then please give us a call or visit **www.youngwriters.co.uk**.

Young Writers
Remus House
Coltsfoot Drive
Peterborough
PE2 9BF
(01733) 890066
info@youngwriters.co.uk